MW00957761

Written and illustrated by Maureen Beat
Publisher: Art Expressions Ltd.
First Printing: 2021

Printed in the United States of America

Letters to Lucky

A True Story

ACKNOWLEDGEMENTS

Heartfelt thanks to Sara McKeon for her suggestion to write this book
and to my family for their feedback. With gratitude to Mary Kay Leatherman,
the children of 63rd Street who loved Lucky,
and for all animal lovers, especially Mary Beth and Jeff.
Finally, thank you to my husband David, who has always been by my side.

For Kristen and Michael who grew up on this beloved block

There once was a dog lost and scared,
who ran in the street and nobody cared.

Two kind gentlemen drove by in a van,
they picked the dog up, they had a plan.

Driving the van to a sheltering place
for food, warmth and many a kind face.

Mr. and Mrs. B.
wanted a dog,

not a cat, nor a bird,
not even a hog!

Visiting a shelter
going cage by cage,

they spotted the dog
they wanted to engage.

Falling in love
with this dog they
would greet,

led to a room
where they all
could meet.

Under the table she would cower and hide,
afraid no matter how hard they tried.

Although this dog seemed timid and shy,
this was the one that caught their eye.

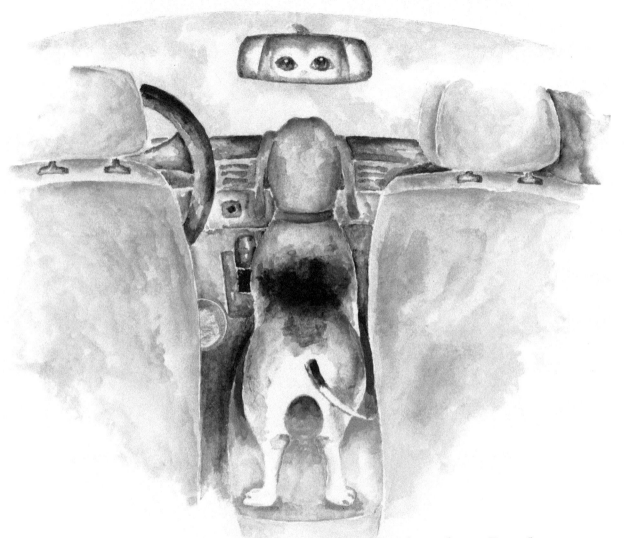

They adopted this dog naming her Lucky,
joking she walked all the way from Kentucky!

Riding in the car she looked straight ahead,
not knowing she'd have a new soft bed.

Saturday walks for coffee and back
were five miles of exercise, if you would track.

She walked like a gymnast, or so it would seem,
treating the curb like her own balance beam!

One walk Mrs. B. tripped on some bricks,
she broke her ankle, the doctor would fix.

Lucky jumped on her bed as her ankle was healing,
dogs just sense how their humans are feeling.

Hearing the crack of an egg she would wait,
licking the yolk right off of the plate!

Mrs. B. snacked on popcorn in her green chair,
tossing kernels to Lucky she'd catch in mid-air!

The block party was the hit of the year,
when Lucky came out, the children would cheer!

Some nights Lucky didn't want to be apart,
sitting next to Mrs. B. who worked on her art.

Mrs. B. went upstairs and crawled into bed,
Lucky followed behind to lay down her head.

She got her own mailbox out front by the tree,
the children wrote letters, colored beautifully.

The children asked politely on her daily walk,
"can we pet your dog?" they'd giggle and talk.

Asking before petting is the smart thing to do,
they pet her back and her tummy too!

She was gentle to children and especially kind,
Lucky was the best dog you ever could find!

Find the luck in every page of this book,
I've hidden a dime, so you should look!

Dimes for me are a wink from my Dad.
I find them in all kinds of places,
...and for that I am glad.

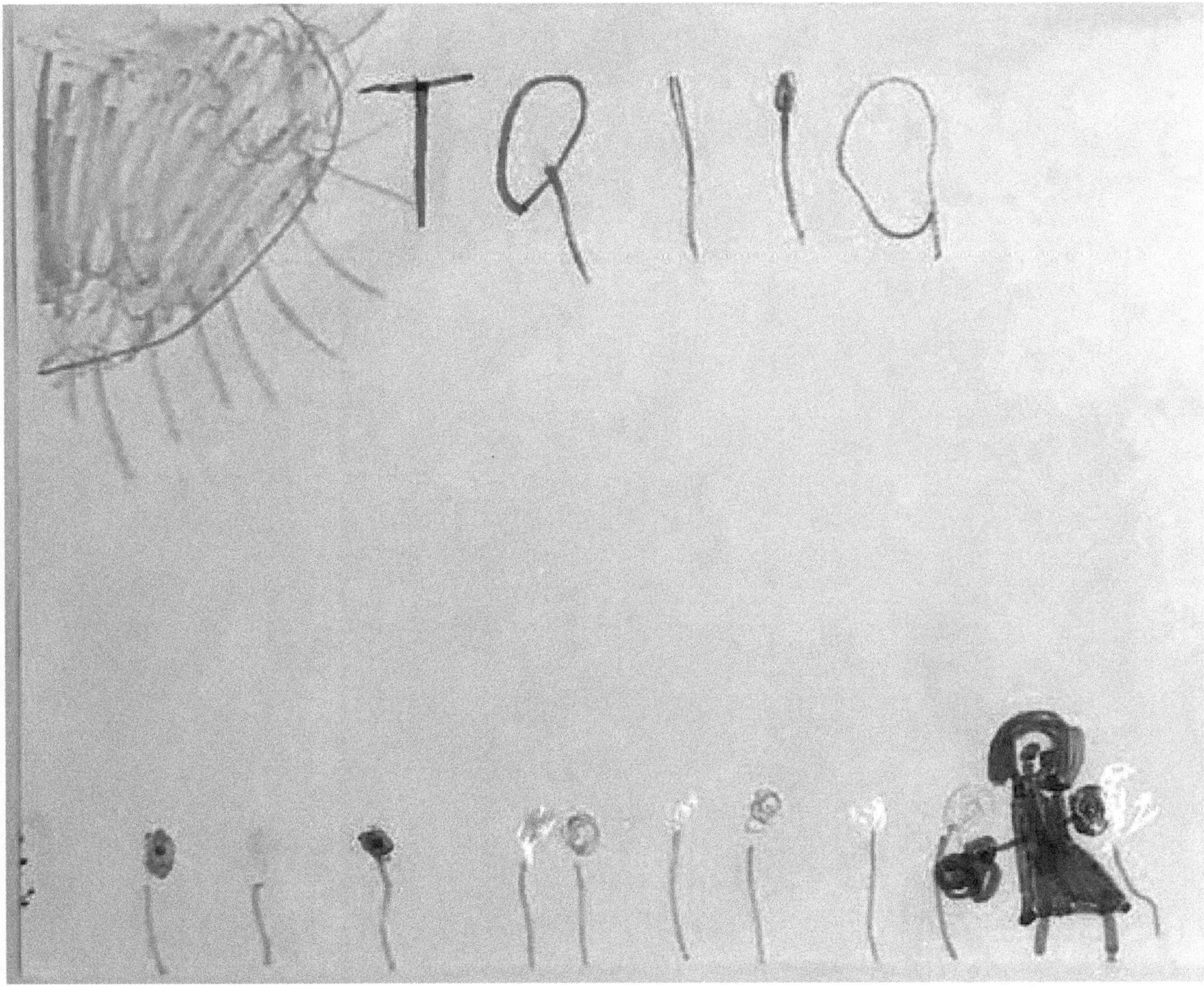

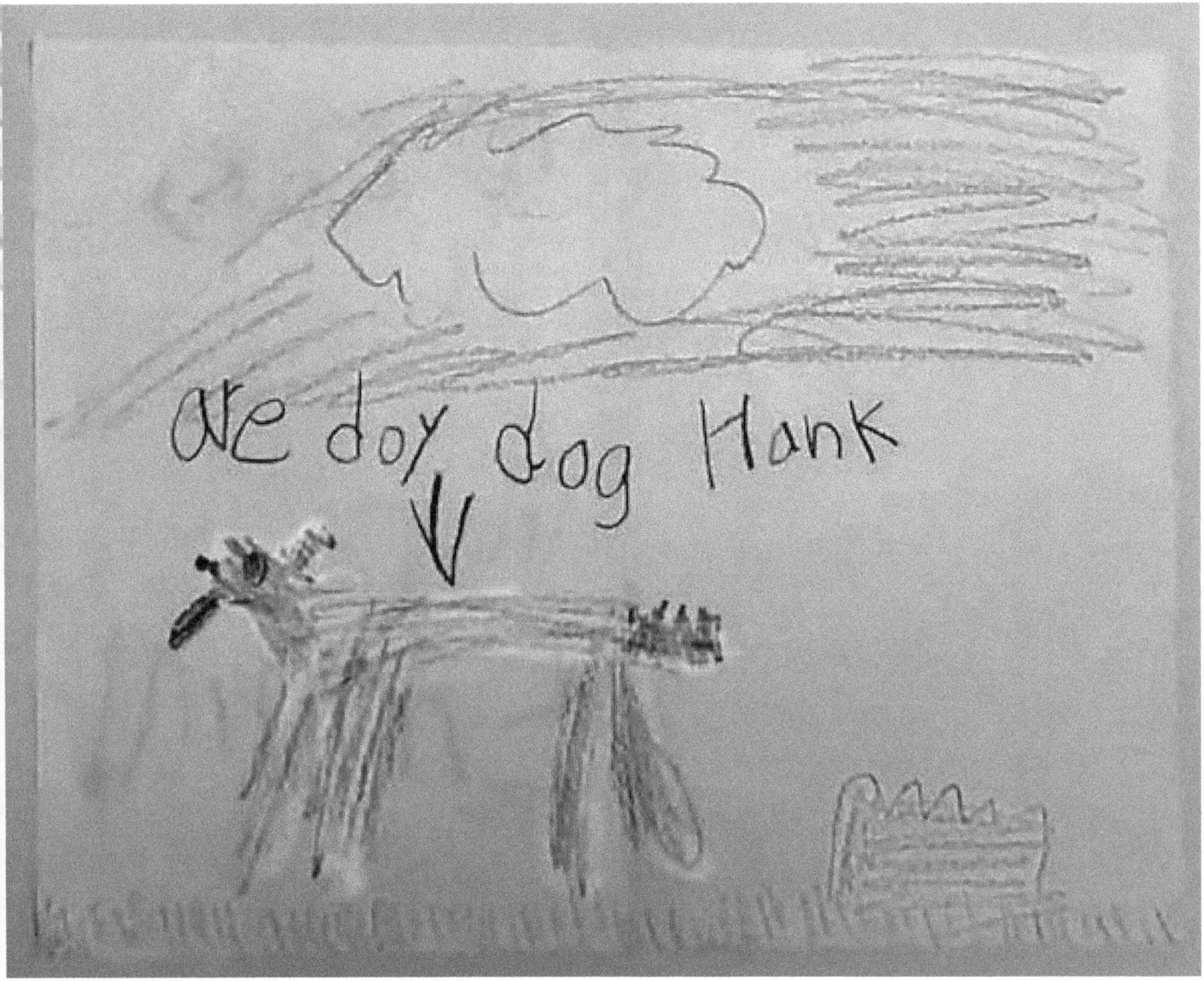
are doy dog Hank

Five little gosts

Five little gosts
went owt one nite
hoten spoockly wut a
frite. Mommy gost
seid boooo boo but anly
4 little gosts come home.

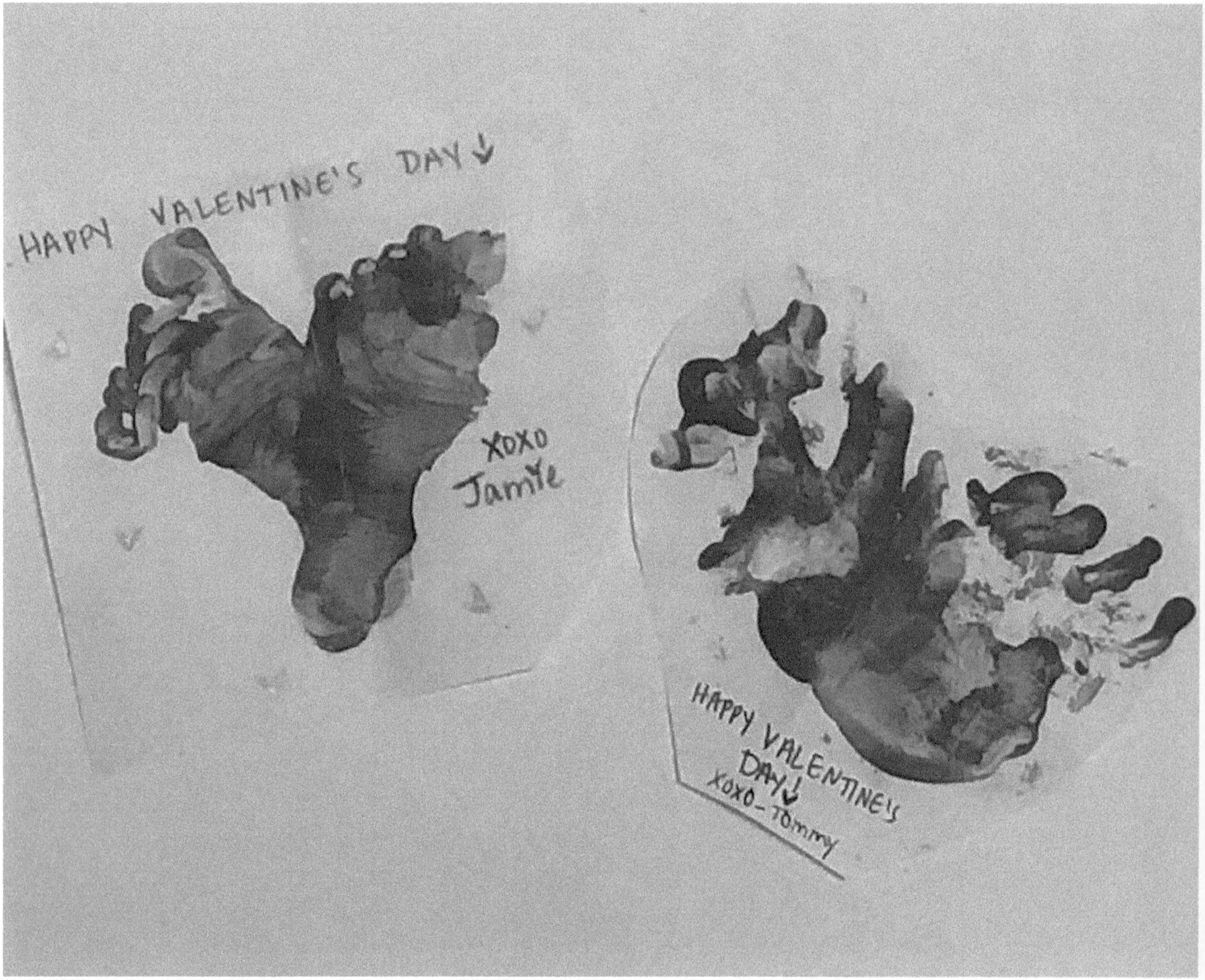

HAPPY VALENTINE'S DAY ↓

XOXO
Jamie

HAPPY VALENTINE'S
DAY ↓
XOXO_Tommy

BEN

Love

Greta

Laucky

PAIGE
PAI

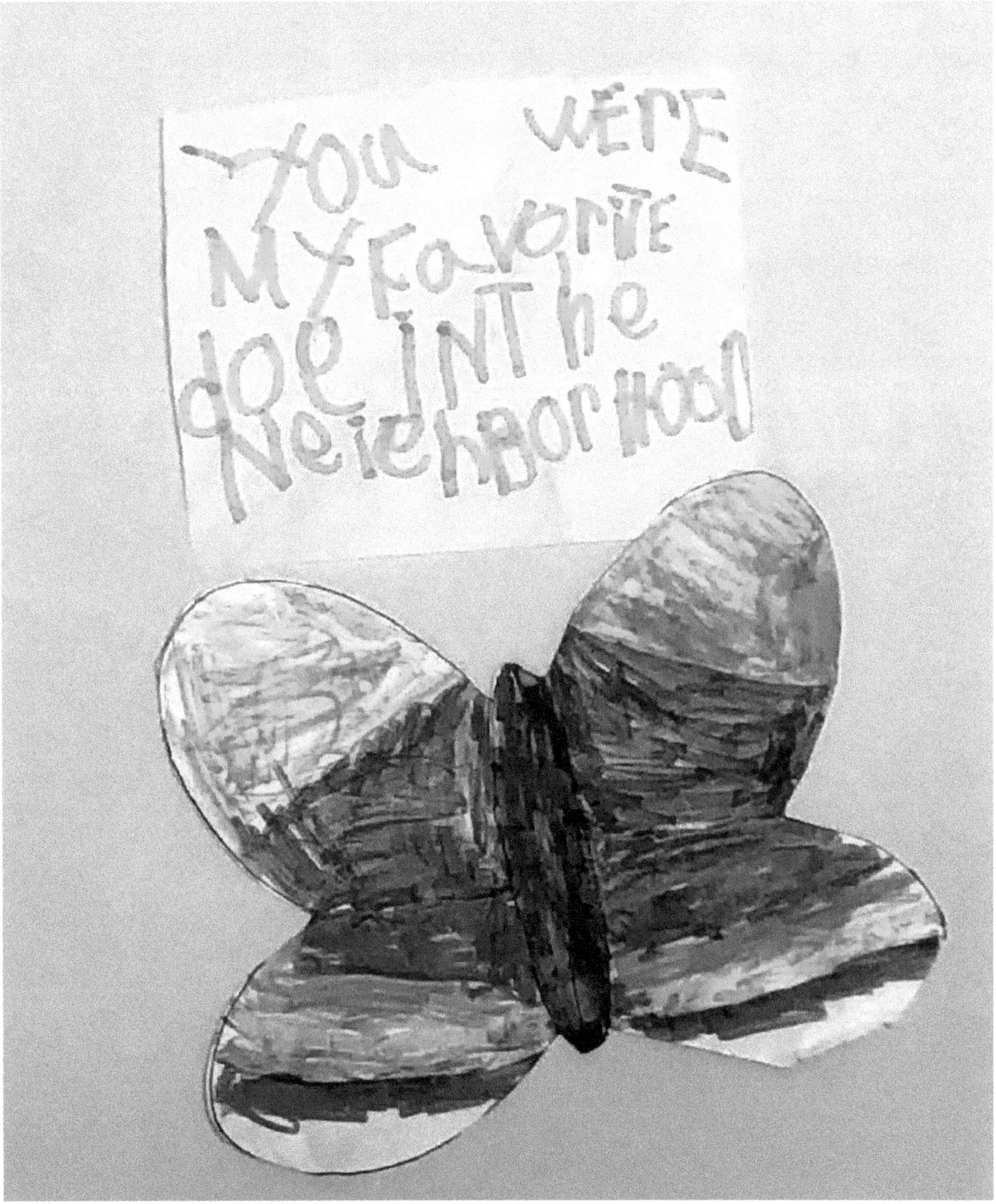
You were
My Favorite
doe In The
Neiehborhood

Dreams do come true!

CPSIA information can be obtained
at www.ICGtesting.com
Printed in the USA
LVHW071031110521
687092LV00007B/195